First aid at work

The Health and Safety (First-Aid) Regulations 1981

Guidance on Regulations

London: TSO

Published by TSO (The Stationery Office), part of Williams Lea, and available from:

Online
https://books.hse.gov.uk/

Mail, Telephone, Fax & E-mail
TSO
PO Box 29, Norwich, NR3 1GN
Telephone orders/General enquiries: 0333 202 5070
Fax orders: 0333 202 5080
E-mail: customer.services@tso.co.uk
Textphone 0333 202 5077

TSO@Blackwell and other Accredited Agents

Published for the Health and Safety Executive under licence from the Controller of her Majesty's Stationery Office.

Printed in the United Kingdom for The Stationery Office.

J003930157

This guidance is issued by the Health and Safety Executive. Following the guidance is not compulsory, unless specifically stated, and you are free to take other action. But if you do follow the guidance you will normally be doing enough to comply with the law. Health and safety inspectors seek to secure compliance with the law and may refer to this guidance.

Cover image supplied courtesy of St John Ambulance.

Contents

Preface

This publication has been updated to take account of regulation 3(2) being amended to remove the requirement for HSE to approve the training and qualifications of appointed first-aid personnel.

In this, the 2013 edition, the text of the Regulations has been amended to reflect the change above, and to incorporate some additional amendments brought about by other previous legislative changes. Furthermore, the first-aid Approved Code of Practice has been withdrawn and associated guidance has been strengthened to assist employers in their selection of first-aid training providers.

Introduction

1   The Health and Safety (First-Aid) Regulations 1981 set out the essential aspects of first aid that employers have to address. This publication will help them to understand and comply with the Regulations and offers practical advice on what they need to do. Employers may also find it useful to look at HSE's 'First aid at work' web pages (see 'Further information'). Practical guidance on first aid at mines is given in a separate publication (see 'Further reading'). These Regulations apply to all workplaces, including those with fewer than five employees.

2   This publication contains the Regulations and guidance. The Regulations are shown in italics, and the guidance on regulations is in plain text.

Regulation 1 Citation and commencement

Regulation	1

These Regulations may be cited as the Health and Safety (First-Aid) Regulations 1981 and shall come into operation on 1st July 1982.

Regulation 2 Interpretation

Regulation	2

(1)   In these Regulations, unless the context otherwise requires – "first-aid" means –

(a)   in cases where a person will need help from a medical practitioner or nurse, treatment for the purpose of preserving life and minimising the consequences of injury and illness until such help is obtained, and

(b)   treatment of minor injuries which would otherwise receive no treatment or which do not need treatment by a medical practitioner or nurse;

"mine" means a mine within the meaning of Section 180 of the Mines and Quarries Act 1954.

(2)   In these Regulations, unless the context otherwise requires, any reference to –

(a)   a numbered Regulation or Schedule is a reference to the Regulation of, or Schedule to, these Regulations bearing that number;

(b)   a numbered paragraph is a reference to the paragraph bearing that number in the Regulation in which the reference appears.

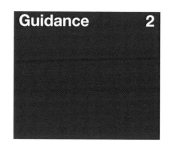

Guidance 2

3   Employers have a legal duty to make arrangements to ensure their employees receive immediate attention if they are injured or taken ill at work. It doesn't matter whether the injury or illness is caused by the work they do, what is important is that they receive immediate attention and that an ambulance is called in serious cases. First aid can save lives and prevent minor injuries becoming major ones. First-aid provision in the workplace covers the arrangements that need to be made to manage injuries or illness suffered at work. The Regulations do not prevent staff who are specially trained from taking action beyond the initial management stage.

Regulation 3 Duty of employer to make provision for first-aid

Regulation 3

(1)   An employer shall provide, or ensure that there are provided, such equipment and facilities as are adequate and appropriate in the circumstances for enabling first-aid to be rendered to his employees if they are injured or become ill at work.

(2)   Subject to paragraphs (3) and (4), an employer shall provide, or ensure that there is provided, such number of suitable persons as is adequate and appropriate in the circumstances for rendering first-aid to his employees if they are injured or become ill at work; and for this purpose a person shall not be suitable unless he has undergone such training and has such qualifications as may be appropriate in the circumstances of that case.

(3)   Where a person provided under paragraph (2) is absent in temporary and exceptional circumstances it shall be sufficient compliance with that paragraph if the employer appoints a person, or ensures that a person is appointed, to take charge of –

(a)   the situation relating to an injured or ill employee who will need help from a medical practitioner or nurse, and
(b)   the equipment and facilities provided under paragraph (1)
(c)   throughout the period of any such absence.

(4)   Where having regard to –

(a)   the nature of the undertaking, and
(b)   the number of employees at work, and
(c)   the location of the establishment,

it would be adequate and appropriate if instead of a person for rendering first-aid there was a person appointed to take charge as in paragraph (3)(a) and (b), then instead of complying with paragraph (2) the employer may appoint such a person, or ensure that such a person is appointed.

(5)   Any first-aid room provided pursuant to this regulation shall be easily accessible to stretchers and to any other equipment needed to convey patients to and from the room and be sign-posted, and any such sign to comply with regulation 4 of the Health and Safety (Safety Signs and Signals) Regulations 1996 as if it were provided in accordance with that regulation.

Guidance   **3**

Needs assessment

4   An employer should make an assessment of first-aid needs appropriate to the circumstances (hazards and risks) of each workplace.

5   The aim of first aid is to reduce the effects of injury or illness suffered at work, whether caused by the work itself or not. First-aid provision must be 'adequate and appropriate in the circumstances'. This means that sufficient first-aid equipment, facilities and personnel should be available at all times, taking account of alternative working patterns, to:

- give immediate assistance to casualties with both common injuries or illnesses and those likely to arise from specific hazards at work;
- summon an ambulance or other professional help.

6   Where an employer provides first-aiders in the workplace, they should ensure they have undertaken suitable training, have an appropriate first-aid qualification and remain competent to perform their role. Typically, first-aiders will hold a valid certificate of competence in either first aid at work (FAW) or emergency first aid at work (EFAW). EFAW training enables a first-aider to give emergency first aid to someone who is injured or becomes ill while at work. FAW training includes EFAW and also equips the first-aider to apply first aid to a range of specific injuries and illnesses (see paragraphs 52–73).

This guidance is written to reflect the optional four-layer framework for first-aid provision that has been in place for many years. The framework will help employers to comply with the Regulations by providing 'off-the-peg' levels of provision. These layers are:

- **appointed person (AP);**
- **emergency first aid at work (EFAW);**
- **first aid at work (FAW);**
- **additional training.**

You may choose not to use this optional framework and use an alternative means to demonstrate compliance with your needs assessment. The thinking behind this guidance, however, applies equally to whatever level of training you choose (unless alternative guidance is provided for specific instances).

7   If an employer, after carrying out a needs assessment, decides a first-aider is not required in the workplace, a person should be appointed to take charge of the first-aid arrangements. The role of this appointed person includes looking after the first-aid equipment and facilities and calling the emergency services when required (see paragraphs 78–81).

8   How much first-aid provision an employer has to make depends on the circumstances (the hazards and risks) of each workplace. Employers are well placed to determine the level of hazard and risk as they will be familiar with the exact circumstances of the workplace. There is no fixed level, but each employer needs to assess the equipment, facilities and personnel that are appropriate. Where employers have an occupational health service, or access to other occupational health advice, they might wish to delegate to them the responsibility for carrying out the assessment and advising on first-aid provision and needs.

9   There is no requirement for the assessment of first-aid needs to be formal or written down, although it may be useful for employers to retain a written record. By

Guidance 3

retaining a record of their needs assessment employers can demonstrate to a safety representative or an HSE or local authority inspector how they decided on their level of first-aid provision.

10   In assessing their needs, employers should consider:

- the nature of the work and workplace hazards and risks;
- the nature of the workforce;
- the organisation's history of accidents;
- the size of the organisation;
- the needs of travelling, remote and lone workers;
- work patterns;
- the distribution of the workforce;
- the remoteness of the site from emergency medical services;
- employees working on shared or multi-occupied sites;
- annual leave and other absences of first-aiders and appointed persons;
- first-aid provision for non-employees.

11   Table 1 contains a checklist to help employers assess their needs and record relevant information. Appendix 1 can act as a record of first-aid provision. The HSE first-aid web pages also contain examples of needs assessment case studies for different industry sectors and levels of hazard, to help explain what the result of a first-aid needs assessment would look like.

Table 1 Checklist for assessment of first-aid needs

Factor to consider	Space for notes	Impact on first-aid provision
Hazards (use the findings of your general risk assessment and take account of any parts of your workplace that have different work activities/hazards which may require different levels of first-aid provision)		
Does your workplace have low-level hazards such as those that might be found in offices and shops?		The minimum provision is: – an appointed person to take charge of first-aid arrangements; – a suitably stocked first-aid box.
Does your workplace have higher-level hazards such as chemicals or dangerous machinery?		You should consider: – providing first-aiders; – providing additional training for first-aiders to deal with injuries resulting from special hazards; – providing a suitably stocked first-aid box; – providing additional first-aid equipment; – precise location of first-aid equipment; – providing a first-aid room; – informing the emergency services of specific hazards etc in advance.

Guidance 3

Factor to consider	Space for notes	Impact on first-aid provision
Do your work activities involve special hazards such as hydrofluoric acid or confined spaces?		You should consider: – providing first-aiders; – additional training for first-aiders to deal with injuries resulting from special hazards; – additional first-aid equipment; – precise location of first-aid equipment; – providing a first-aid room; – informing the emergency services of specific hazards etc in advance.
Employees		
How many people are employed on site?		Where there are small numbers of employees, the minimum provision is: – an appointed person to take charge of first-aid arrangements; – a suitably stocked first-aid box. Where there are large numbers of employees, ie more than 25, even in low-hazard environments, you should consider providing: – first-aiders; – additional first-aid equipment; – a first-aid room.
Are there inexperienced workers on site, or employees with disabilities or particular health problems?		You should consider: – additional training for first-aiders; – additional first-aid equipment; – local siting of first-aid equipment. Your first-aid provision should cover any work experience trainees.

Guidance 3	Factor to consider	Space for notes	Impact on first-aid provision
	Accidents and ill-health record		
	What is your record of accidents and ill health? What injuries and illness have occurred and where did they happen?		Ensure your first-aid provision will cater for the types of injuries and illnesses that have occurred in your workplace. Monitor accidents and ill health and review your first-aid provision as appropriate.
	Working arrangements		
	Do you have employees who travel a lot, work remotely or work alone?		You should consider: – issuing personal first-aid kits; – issuing personal communicators/mobile phones to employees.
	Do any of your employees work shifts or out-of-hours?		You should ensure there is adequate first-aid provision at all times people are at work.
	Are the premises spread out, eg are there several buildings on the site or multi-floor buildings?		You should consider the need for provision in each building or on each floor.
	Is your workplace remote from emergency medical services?		You should: – inform the emergency services of your location; – consider special arrangements with the emergency services; – consider emergency transport requirements.
	Do any of your employees work at sites occupied by other employers?		You should make arrangements with other site occupiers to ensure adequate provision of first aid. A written agreement between employers is strongly recommended.
	Do you have sufficient provision to cover absences of first-aiders or appointed persons?		You should consider: – what cover is needed for annual leave and other planned absences; – what cover is needed for unplanned and exceptional absences.

Guidance 3

Factor to consider	Space for notes	Impact on first-aid provision
Non-employees		
Do members of the public or non-employees visit your premises?		Under the Health and Safety (First-Aid) Regulations 1981, you have no legal duty to provide first aid for non-employees but HSE strongly recommends that you include them in your first-aid provision.

Nature of the work

12   The Management of Health and Safety at Work Regulations 1999 require employers to make an assessment of the risks to health and safety of their employees at work, and to identify what measures they need to take to prevent or control these risks.[1] Information gathered from the risk assessment can help the employer carry out their assessment of first-aid needs if preventive or control measures fail. Identifying the likely nature of an accident or injury will help the employer work out the type, quantity and location of first-aid equipment, and the facilities and personnel to provide.

13   To help employers, Table 2 gives examples of a number of hazards commonly found in the workplace, the causes of accidents that might occur in working with them, and the injuries that might arise. It is not intended to cover all hazards that may be present in the workplace or all injuries that might occur. It should also be remembered that an employee might become ill at any time. An assessment of first-aid needs should consider this possibility, whether or not an illness is caused by work. More detailed information on workplace hazards, risk assessment and how to prevent work-related injuries and illness is available on HSE's website (see 'Further information').

Table 2 Hazards commonly found in the workplace

Hazard	Causes of accidents	Examples of injury requiring first aid
Chemicals	Exposure during handling, spillages, splashing, leaks	Poisoning, loss of consciousness, burns, eye injuries, respiratory problems
Electricity	Failure to securely isolate electrical systems and equipment during work on them, poorly maintained electrical equipment, contact with overhead power lines, underground power cables or mains electricity supplies, using unsuitable electrical equipment in explosive atmospheres	Electric shock, burns, heart attack

	Hazard	Causes of accidents	Examples of injury requiring first aid
Guidance **3**	Machinery	Loose hair or clothing becoming tangled in machinery, being hit by moving parts or material thrown from machinery, contact with sharp edges	Crush injuries, amputations, fractures, lacerations, eye injuries
	Manual handling	Repetitive and/or heavy lifting, bending and twisting, exerting too much force, handling bulky or unstable loads, handling in uncomfortable working positions	Fractures, lacerations, sprains and strains
	Slip and trip hazards	Uneven floors, staircases, trailing cables, obstructions, slippery surfaces due to spillages, worn carpets and mats	Fractures, lacerations, sprains and strains
	Work at height	Overreaching or overbalancing when using ladders, falling off or through a roof	Head injury, loss of consciousness, spinal injury, fractures, sprains and strains, lacerations
	Workplace transport	Hit by, against or falling from a vehicle, being hit by part of a load falling from a vehicle, being injured as a result of a vehicle collapse or overturn	Crush injuries, head injury, fractures, sprains and strains

14   Using your health and safety risk assessments you will have identified the hazards in your workplace and the possible harmful consequences for employees and others. This information will help you determine the level of first-aid provision. For example, in organisations such as offices or shops, employers may only need to provide an appointed person to take charge of first-aid arrangements, and a clearly identified and suitably stocked first-aid box. However, even in these circumstances it is still possible for an accident or sudden illness to occur and employers may wish to consider having a qualified first-aider available.

15   Where the work involves higher level hazards such as chemicals or dangerous machinery, or special hazards such as hydrofluoric acid or confined spaces, first-aid requirements will be greater. Employers may then need to:

- provide sufficient numbers of qualified first-aiders so that someone is always available to give first aid immediately following an incident;
- provide additional training for first-aiders to deal with injuries resulting from special hazards;
- consider additional first-aid equipment;
- provide one or more first-aid rooms;
- inform the local emergency services, in writing, of the site where hazardous substances or processes are in use.

16   In deciding on their first-aid provision, employers will need to take account

of different work activities in different parts of an establishment. For example, a work site may contain production and office/administration areas. In such circumstances, separate risk assessments will have to be made for individual departments, and the results of these should be carried over to the assessment of first-aid needs.

Nature of the workforce

17   The particular needs of young workers, trainees, pregnant workers and employees with disabilities or particular health problems, where known (eg asthma, diabetes, peanut allergy, epilepsy or a history of heart disease), should be addressed (noting other relevant legislation accordingly). For example, using the age profile of your workforce as a crude indicator can help you identify the likelihood of employees being at greater risk of developing heart conditions. First-aid provision should also be extended to work experience trainees.

History of accidents

18   Information collected when investigating previous accidents/incidents should be used when assessing the adequacy of future first-aid provision. For large and/or multi-site organisations, this information could be helpful in determining where first-aiders should be located, what geographical area they should be required to cover and what first-aid equipment is necessary.

Size of the organisation

19   Generally, the larger the workforce, the greater the first-aid provision that is required. However, employee numbers should not be the sole basis for determining first-aid needs. A greater level of provision may be required when fewer people are at work but are undertaking more high-risk tasks such as maintenance work. Employers should provide sufficient cover for the various circumstances that can occur.

20   Even in workplaces with a small number of employees, particularly if there are significant hazards and/or risks present, there is still the possibility of an accident or sudden illness. Therefore, employers may wish to consider providing a qualified first-aider.

Needs of travelling, remote and lone workers

21   Employers are responsible for meeting the first-aid needs of their employees working away from the main site, for example those who travel regularly or who work elsewhere. The assessment should determine whether those who travel long distances or are continuously mobile should carry a personal first-aid kit. Organisations with employees who work in remote areas should consider making special arrangements such as issuing personal communicators and providing additional training. Where employees work alone, other means of summoning help, such as a mobile phone, may be useful to call for assistance in an emergency.

Work patterns

22   First-aid requirements may vary where employees work shifts or out-of-hours. It is important that sufficient provision is always available when employees are at work, and separate arrangements may have to be made for each shift.

Guidance | **3**

Distribution of the workforce

23   An employer should consider how the size of the premises could affect quick access to first-aid facilities. For example, whether additional first-aid provision is needed on a site with more than one building, or whether the distance between buildings is such that additional provision would be unnecessary. Employers with a multi-floor building should consider how many first-aiders or appointed persons will be required to give adequate provision to employees on each floor. Consideration should also be given to employees who work in self-contained areas and how their needs are assessed and met.

Remoteness of the site from emergency medical services

24   Where a site is remote from emergency medical services, employers may need to make special arrangements to ensure appropriate transport is available. Employers should inform the emergency services, in writing, of their location and any particular circumstances, including specific hazards.

Employees working on shared or multi-occupied sites

25   On a shared or multi-occupied site, employers can arrange for one employer to take responsibility for providing first-aid cover for all the workers. In these cases, a full exchange of information about the hazards and risks involved should help make sure that the shared provision is adequate. All employers should agree the arrangements and employees should be kept informed. A written agreement between employers is strongly recommended to avoid any misunderstandings.

26   Where an employment business contracts out employees to another employer, the employment business should make sure, by arrangement with the user employer, that these employees have access to first-aid provision.

Annual leave, holiday and other absences of first-aiders and appointed persons

27   It is essential that adequate provision is made to cover all times people are at work. Employers therefore need to ensure there is cover for annual leave or holiday and other planned absences of first-aiders or appointed persons. Employers should also consider what cover is needed for unplanned and exceptional absences such as sick leave or special leave due to bereavement.

First-aid provision for non-employees

28   These Regulations do not require employers to provide first aid for anyone other than their own employees. However, many organisations, such as schools, places of entertainment, fairgrounds and shops, provide a service for others and it is strongly recommended that employers include non-employees in their assessment of first-aid needs and make provision for them. This may require first-aiders to receive additional training above the legal minimum requirement so that they are able to act competently, for example additional training in paediatric first aid if operating in a school.

29   Where first-aid provision is intended to cover both employees and non-employees, employers should check their liability insurance covers all the activities of first-aiders. They should also ensure that:

- the level of provision for employees does not fall below the standard required by these Regulations;
- the level of provision for non-employees complies with any other relevant legislation and guidance.

Review of first-aid provision

30   Employers should periodically review their first-aid needs, particularly after any operating changes, to make sure provision remains appropriate. To help with this process, it is recommended that a record is kept of the incidents dealt with by first-aiders and appointed persons (see paragraphs 31–32).

Records

31   It is sensible for employers to provide first-aiders and appointed persons with a book in which to record incidents they attend. Any such book should be kept in accordance with the requirements of the Data Protection Act 1998 (see 'Further reading'). Where there are a number of first-aiders working for a single employer, it would be advisable for one central book to be used, though this may not be practicable on larger, well spread out sites. The information to be recorded should include:

- date, time and place of the incident;
- name and job of the injured or ill person;
- details of the injury/illness and what first aid was given;
- what happened to the person immediately afterwards (for example, went back to work, went home, went to hospital);
- name and signature of the first-aider or person dealing with the incident.

32   This information can help the employer identify accident trends and possible areas for improvement in the control of health and safety risks. It can be used for reference in future first-aid needs assessments. These records may also be helpful for insurance and investigative purposes. The record book is not the same as the statutory accident book (see 'Further reading'), although the two might be combined.

RIDDOR

33   All employers, self-employed people and people in control of work premises have duties under the Reporting of Injuries, Diseases and Dangerous Occurrences Regulations 2013 (RIDDOR).[2]

34   They must report certain work-related injuries, cases of ill health and dangerous occurrences. HSE will pass details to the relevant enforcing authority. RIDDOR applies to all work activities but not all incidents are reportable.

First-aid materials, equipment and facilities

35   When the assessment of first-aid requirements has been completed, the employer should provide the materials, equipment and facilities needed to make sure that the level of cover identified as necessary will be available to employees at all relevant times. This will include ensuring that first-aid equipment, suitably marked and easily accessible, is available in all places where working conditions require it.

First-aid containers

36   The minimum level of first-aid equipment is a suitably stocked and properly identified first-aid container. Every employer should provide for each work site at least one first-aid container supplied with a sufficient quantity of first-aid materials suitable for the particular circumstances.

37   Depending on the findings of the first-aid needs assessment, more than one first-aid container might be required on large sites. First-aid containers should be easily accessible and preferably placed near to hand-washing facilities. They should only be stocked with items useful for giving first aid and should be protected from dust and

Guidance   **3**

damp. All first-aid containers should be identified by a white cross on a green background.[3] Guidance on the contents of first-aid kits can be found in Appendix 2.

38   The contents of first-aid containers should be examined frequently and restocked soon after use. Sufficient supplies should be held in stock on site. Care should be taken to dispose of items safely once they reach their expiry date.

Additional first-aid materials and equipment

39   The needs assessment may indicate that additional materials and equipment are required, for example foil blankets, haemostatic dressings, tourniquets, disposable aprons and individually wrapped moist wipes. They may be kept in the first-aid container if there is room, or stored separately. Other pieces of equipment may include adhesive hypoallergenic microporous tape, shears capable of cutting through clothing and sterile disposable tweezers.

40   If mains tap water is not readily available for eye irrigation, at least one litre of sterile water or sterile normal saline (0.9% w/v) in sealed, disposable containers should be provided. Once the seal has been broken, containers should not be kept for reuse. Containers should not be used beyond their expiry date.

41   There may be a need for items such as protective equipment in case first-aiders have to enter dangerous atmospheres, or calcium gluconate for the management of hydrofluoric acid burns. Such items should be stored securely near the first-aid container, in the first-aid room or in the hazard area, as appropriate. Access to them should be restricted to people trained in their use.

Tablets and medication

42   First aid at work does not include giving tablets or medicines to treat illness. The only exception to this is where aspirin is used as first aid to a casualty with a suspected heart attack in accordance with currently accepted first-aid practice. It is recommended that tablets and medicines should not be kept in the first-aid container.

43   Some workers carry their own medication that has been prescribed by their doctor (eg an inhaler for asthma). If an individual needs to take their own prescribed medication, the first-aider's role is generally limited to helping them do so and contacting the emergency services, as appropriate.

Automated external defibrillators (AEDs)

44   Where an employer has identified through their needs assessment that they wish to provide an automated external defibrillator (AED) in the workplace, then the Provision and Use of Workplace Equipment Regulations 1998 (PUWER) apply.[4] For the purpose of complying with PUWER in these situations, the employer should provide information and written instructions, for example from the manufacturer of the AED, on how to use it. Fuller training, however, is likely to make the user more confident and is now an integral part of the syllabus for FAW and EFAW courses.

Travelling first-aid kits

45   Employers should consider issuing these types of kits to all mobile members of staff or, alternatively, placing them in vehicles used by mobile members of staff for business purposes. Depending on the needs assessment, you should also consider whether these employees undergo a course of instruction in emergency first aid at work, particularly if they are involved in higher-hazard activities. Guidance on the contents of travelling first-aid kits can be found in Appendix 2.

46   Suitable arrangements should be in place for restocking kits.

First-aid rooms

47   Employers should provide a suitable first-aid room or rooms where the assessment of first-aid needs identifies this as necessary. The first-aid room(s) should contain essential first-aid facilities and equipment, be easily accessible to stretchers and be clearly signposted and identified. If possible, the room(s) should be reserved exclusively for giving first aid.

48   A first-aid room will usually be necessary where there are higher hazards such as in chemical industries or on large construction sites, and in larger premises at a distance from medical services. A designated person should be given responsibility for supervising it. The room(s) should be clearly signposted and identified by white lettering or symbols on a green background.[3]

49   First-aid rooms should:

- be large enough to hold an examination/medical couch, with enough space at each side for people to work, a chair and any necessary additional equipment;
- have washable surfaces and adequate heating, ventilation and lighting;
- be kept clean, tidy, accessible and available for use at all times when employees are at work;
- be positioned as near as possible to a point of access for transport to hospital;
- display a notice on the door advising of the names, locations and, if appropriate, telephone extensions of first-aiders and how to contact them.

50   Typical examples of the equipment and facilities a first-aid room may contain are:

- a sink with hot and cold running water;
- drinking water with disposable cups;
- soap and paper towels;
- a store for first-aid materials;
- foot-operated refuse containers, lined with disposable, yellow clinical waste bags or a container suitable for the safe disposal of clinical waste;
- an examination/medical couch with waterproof protection and clean pillows and blankets (a paper couch roll may be used that is changed between casualties);
- a chair;
- a telephone or other communication equipment;
- a record book for recording incidents attended by a first-aider or appointed person (see paragraphs 31–32).

51   If the first-aid room(s) cannot be reserved exclusively for giving first aid, employers need to make sure that the first-aid facilities can be made available quickly if necessary. For example, they should consider the implications of whether:

- the activities usually carried out in the room can be stopped immediately in an emergency;
- the furnishings and equipment can be moved easily and quickly to a position that will not interfere with giving first aid;
- the storage arrangements for first-aid furnishings and equipment allow them to be made available quickly when necessary.

First-aid personnel

First-aiders

52   Where the first-aid assessment identifies a need for people to be available for rendering first aid, the employer should ensure that they are provided in sufficient numbers and at appropriate locations to enable first aid to be administered without

Guidance 3

delay should the occasion arise. Where 25 or more people are employed, even in low-hazard environments, at least one such person should be provided.

How many first-aiders are needed?

53   The findings of the first-aid needs assessment will help the employer decide how many first-aiders are required. There are no standard rules on exact numbers as employers will need to take into account all the relevant circumstances of their particular workplace.

54   After completing the checklist in Table 1, the flow chart in Appendix 3 serves as a general guide on how many first-aiders or appointed persons might be needed. The numbers quoted in Appendix 3 are suggestions only. The employer should take into account all relevant information to make a valid judgement.

What factors should be considered when selecting someone to be a first-aider?

55   When selecting someone to take up the role of a first-aider, a number of factors need to be taken into account, including an individual's:

- reliability, disposition and communication skills;
- aptitude and ability to absorb new knowledge and learn new skills;
- ability to cope with stressful and physically demanding emergency procedures;
- normal duties, which should be such that they may be able to respond immediately and rapidly to an emergency.

First-aid training

Bodies concerned with delivery of first-aid-at-work training

56   Some first-aid training providers choose to operate through voluntary accreditation schemes whose intention is to set and maintain standards which can help employers meet their legal requirements. These schemes are not mandatory and employers may decide to choose an independent training organisation, but these bodies may help employers select training organisations that offer a standard of training with appropriate content, suitable trainers and assessors, and relevant and robust quality assurance systems.

57   Some training providers offer 'regulated qualifications. These are nationally recognised and can be obtained from a training centre for an 'awarding organisation' (AO). These AOs are recognised by national qualification regulators (Ofqual, SQA or Qualification Wales),* have dedicated policies and quality assurance processes and must approve and monitor their training centres to ensure training meets standards set by the national regulators. The regulators stipulate that AOs and their training centres must work in compliance with the Assessment Principles for First Aid Qualifications – see the SQA website www.sqa.org.uk.

58   Employers may obtain appropriate training from the Voluntary Aid Societies,† who together are acknowledged by HSE as one of the standard-setters for currently accepted first-aid practice (see paragraph 61) as far as they relate to the topics covered in FAW (Appendix 5) and EFAW (Appendix 6) training courses.

---

*   Ofqual is the regulator of qualifications, examinations and assessments in England. SQA (the Scottish Qualifications Authority) and Qualification Wales carry out similar functions in Scotland and Wales, as does the Council for the Curriculum, Examinations and Assessment (CCEA), in Northern Ireland.

†   The Voluntary Aid Societies are St John Ambulance, British Red Cross and St Andrew's First Aid.

Guidance 3

59   When an employer selects a training provider, they will need to be confident that the provider will deliver training with appropriate content (ie content identified as being appropriate within the needs assessment, and/or content in line with Appendices 5 and 6), use suitable trainers and assessors, and has relevant and robust quality assurance systems in place.[4] (Similar quality standards are expected of all first-aid training providers including non-affiliated, independent first-aid training organisations.) All training providers should be able and prepared to demonstrate how they satisfy these criteria.

Training provider selection

60   HSE provides guidance[5] on our first-aid web pages for employers to assist them in selecting a competent first-aid training provider.

61   Training organisations should use training material, and teach the first-aid management of injuries and illness, as covered in FAW/EFAW training courses and in accordance with:

■   current guidelines published by the Resuscitation Council (UK); and
■   the current edition of the first-aid manual of the Voluntary Aid Societies (St John Ambulance, British Red Cross, St Andrew's First Aid); or
■   other published guidelines, provided they are in line with the two above or supported by a responsible body of medical opinion.

62   Blended learning is a combination of face to face and e-learning and is an accepted means by which workplace first-aid training can be delivered. It is important that employers conduct the necessary additional checks (due diligence) to decide if this method is suitable. This means you should make sure you are satisfied that:

■   the individual being trained knows how to use the technology that delivers the training;
■   the training provider has an adequate means of supporting the individual during their training;
■   the training provider has a robust system in place to prevent identity fraud;
■   sufficient time is allocated to classroom based learning and assessment of the practical elements of the syllabus. HSE strongly recommends that elements of the syllabus requiring practical demonstration of first-aid administration should be assessed by direct observation to ensure the competence of candidates;
■   the provider has an appropriate means of assessing the e-learning component of the training.

Employers should also ensure they are complying with Regulation 13 of the Health and Safety Management Regulations 1999, which has a requirement to ensure adequate time is set aside during the working day to undertake any first-aid training employees receive.

63   Where an employer's first-aid needs assessment identifies (or an employer chooses to use) qualifications other than FAW or EFAW to demonstrate workplace first-aid competence, it will be necessary for an employer to ensure that common elements of the syllabus are taught in accordance with the same guidelines.

64   Where an employer decides to provide this training in-house, they will need to establish that it is appropriate by ensuring that the content reflects the content of the FAW or EFAW qualifications listed in Appendices 5 and 6 and is delivered in accordance with currently accepted standards for first aid.

Guidance **3**

65   In-house individuals acting as trainers/assessors should have the necessary skills, qualifications and competence expected of those working for an external training provider. A quality assurance system is needed to ensure that the competence of trainers/assessors is regularly reviewed by competent 'verifiers'. These systems should be reviewed on an annual basis by a competent person independent of those directly involved in the delivery/assessment of this training.

66   You may find it beneficial to maintain records of training. If you keep training records, they should be retained for a minimum of three years after the assessment process has been completed and any certificates should be in accordance with paragraph 68. For further information see GEIS3 *Selecting a first aid training provider*.[5]

67   There is no requirement for the checks you carry out when choosing a training provider to be formalised or written down, although it may be useful for you to retain a written record. By documenting the checks you have undertaken to confirm the competence of a training organisation, and retaining a record of those checks, you can demonstrate to an HSE or local authority inspector how you selected a training provider.

Certificates
68   For an individual to demonstrate they have a competence in first aid they will hold a certificate that contains all of the following minimum information:

- name of training organisation;
- name of qualification;
- name of individual;
- a validity period for three years from date of course completion;
- an indication that the certificate has been issued for the purposes of complying with the requirements of the Health and Safety (First-Aid) Regulations 1981;
- a statement that teaching was delivered in accordance with currently accepted first-aid practice; and
- if the qualification is neither FAW nor EFAW, an outline of the topics covered (this may be on the reverse or as an appendix).

69   Where an alternative qualification is identified in place of FAW/EFAW in an employer's needs assessment, the employer will need to seek assurance that the standard of training received and the competence of the organisation which delivered this training meet the necessary criteria as outlined in our guidance.[5]

Which health professionals are exempt from a qualification in first aid?
70   Provided they can demonstrate current knowledge and skills in first aid, the training and experience of the following qualify them to administer first aid in the workplace without the need to hold a FAW or EFAW or equivalent qualification:

- doctors registered and licensed with the General Medical Council;
- nurses registered with the Nursing and Midwifery Council;
- paramedics registered with the Health and Care Professions Council.

71   If an employee has a current first-aid qualification other than FAW/EFAW, the employer may consider whether it would be suitable in relation to the role of workplace first-aider and their needs assessment.

Guidance   **3**

Additional training needs

72   When arranging FAW or EFAW or other equivalent training, employers should let the training organisation know of any particular hazards at their workplace so training can be tailored to meet those needs.

73   Employers should make sure first-aiders undertake any training additional to the FAW/EFAW or equivalent qualification, as appropriate to the circumstances of the workplace. For example, more in-depth training would be advisable in cases where work activities involve the use of hydrofluoric acid, working in confined spaces or working outdoors or in remote locations. Appendix 4 identifies examples of scenarios where first-aiders may require additional training. It is not comprehensive and employers should refer to the first-aid needs assessment to determine their exact requirements. HSE does not specify the course content or design of additional training courses and they can be undertaken in combination with FAW/EFAW or as stand-alone courses. Separate certificates for additional training may be issued or combined on a single certificate with FAW/EFAW training. In either case, the certificate should record the detail of any additional training undertaken.

Certificate validity, requalification and refresher training

74   All first-aid training certificates, whether FAW, EFAW or some other appropriate training, are valid for three years. Employers need to arrange retraining before certificates expire. The FAW requalification course lasts two days and should cover the same content as the initial FAW course (Appendix 5). If the first-aider does not retrain or requalify before the expiry date on their current certificate they are no longer considered competent to act as a first-aider in the workplace. They can requalify at any time after the expiry date by undertaking the two-day requalification course. However, it may be prudent to complete the three-day FAW course, especially where a considerable period – ie in excess of one month – has elapsed since the FAW certificate expired. It is for the employer to decide the most appropriate training course to requalify the first-aider. An EFAW requalification course should be of the same duration and content (Appendix 6) as the initial EFAW course.

75   HSE strongly recommends that first-aiders undertake annual refresher training during any three-year FAW/EFAW certification period. Although not mandatory, this will help qualified first-aiders maintain their basic skills and keep up-to-date with any changes to first-aid procedures. Appendix 7 contains suggested course content for annual refresher training, although HSE does not specify the design of these courses.

76   Employers should also encourage first-aiders to regularly review their course manual and any other instructional materials and allocate them time to do this. It will further help to maintain their first-aid skills.

77   Employers should keep a record of first-aiders and certification dates to help with the timely arrangement of further training.

Appointed persons

78   Where an employer's assessment of first-aid needs identifies that a designated first-aider is not required, the minimum requirement for an employer is to appoint a person to take charge of the first-aid arrangements, including looking after the equipment and facilities, and calling the emergency services when required. Arrangements should be made for an appointed person to be available to undertake these duties at all times when people are at work.

79   Even in small, low-hazard organisations where first-aiders are considered unnecessary, there is always the possibility of an accident or sudden illness.

Guidance **3**

Therefore, it is important that someone is always available to take charge of the first-aid arrangements, including looking after the equipment and facilities and calling the emergency services when required. In the absence of first-aiders, employers should appoint a person for this purpose. Appointed persons are not necessary where there is an adequate number of first-aiders.

80   To fulfil their role, appointed persons do not need first-aid training, though they may benefit from completion of an EFAW course (or other suitable alternative). Given this, and the remaining possibility of an accident or sudden illness, rather than providing appointed persons, employers may wish to consider providing qualified first-aiders.

81   The Regulations allow for a person to be appointed to provide emergency cover in the absence of first-aiders but only where the absence is due to exceptional, unforeseen and temporary circumstances. Absences such as annual leave do not count. If the first-aid needs assessment indicates that first-aiders are required, they should be available whenever the need arises. This means that at all times during the working day there should be a first-aider on duty.

Regulation 4 Duty of employer to inform his employees of the arrangements made in connection with first-aid

Regulation **4**

An employer shall inform his employees of the arrangements that have been made in connection with the provision of first-aid, including the location of equipment, facilities and personnel.

Guidance **4**

Information for employees

82   First-aid arrangements operate efficiently in an emergency only where everyone in the workplace is aware of them, and understands and accepts them. One way to achieve this is to develop procedures for informing staff in consultation with employees or safety representatives. They should detail first-aid provision and explain how employees will be informed of the location of first-aid equipment, facilities and personnel. The procedures should also identify who will provide relevant first-aid information to new and transferred employees.

83   A simple method of keeping employees informed is to display first-aid notices. The information needs to be clear and easily understood by all employees. Employers should also take steps to cater for those with reading or language difficulties. At least one notice in a prominent position at each site, including the base for travelling employees, should give enough opportunity for employees to see them. The inclusion of first-aid information during induction training will help make sure new employees are made aware of first-aid arrangements.

Regulation 5 Duty of self-employed person to provide first-aid equipment

| Regulation | 5 |

A self-employed person shall provide, or ensure there is provided, such equipment, if any, as is adequate and appropriate in the circumstances to enable him to render first-aid to himself while he is at work.

Duties of self-employed persons

84 The systematic approach to assessment, set out in paragraphs 4–32 may also be valid for deciding how much first-aid provision is needed by the self-employed. Those who carry out activities involving low hazards (such as clerical work) in their own homes would not be expected to provide first-aid equipment beyond their normal needs.

85 Where the self-employed work on premises under the control of an employer or with other self-employed workers, they are each responsible for making their own first-aid provision. However, as indicated in paragraphs 25–26, joint arrangements can be made with other occupiers to provide common cover.

Regulation 6 Power to grant exemptions

| Regulation | 6 |

[Revoked by regulation 24 of the Management of Health and Safety at Work Regulations 1999 (SI 1999/3242).]

Regulation 7 Cases where these Regulations do not apply

| Regulation | 7 |

These Regulations shall not apply –

(a) *where the Diving at Work Regulations 1997 apply;*
(b) *where the Merchant Shipping (Medical Scales) (Fishing Vessels) Regulations 1974 apply;*
(c) *where the Merchant Shipping (Medical Stores) Regulations 1986 apply;*
(d) *on vessels which are registered outside the United Kingdom;*
(e) [Paragraph (e) is revoked by the Management and Administration of Safety and Health at Mines Regulations 1993 (SI 1993/1897), regulations 44(1) and (2)(a), in so far as it applies to mines and mining operations.];
(f) *in respect of the armed forces of the Crown and any force to which any provision of the Visiting Forces Act 1952 applies;*
(g) *where the Offshore Installations and Pipeline Works (First-Aid) Regulations 1989 apply.*

Regulation 8 Application to mines

Regulation	8

Subject to paragraph (2), these Regulations (except regulation 3(3) and (4) and regulation 5) apply to mines.

(6) In their application to mines –

(a) regulation 3(1), (2) and (5) and regulation 4 have effect as if the mine operator were the employer and as if all persons for the time being at work in the mine were the mine operator's employees; and

(b) (b) regulation 3(2) must be read as if the words "Subject to paragraphs (3) and (4)" were omitted.

(7) In this regulation, "mine operator" has the meaning given by regulation 2(1) of the Mines Regulations 2014.[a]

(a) *Substituted by Mines Regulations 2014/3248 Sch.5(2) para.5(b)*

Regulation 9 Application offshore

Regulation	9

Subject to Regulation 7, these Regulations shall apply to and in relation to any premises or activity to or in relation to which sections 1 to 59 of the Health and Safety at Work etc. Act 1974 apply by virtue of Articles 6 and 7(a), (b) and (d) of the Health and Safety at Work etc. Act 1974 (Application outside Great Britain) Order 1977 (which relate respectively to mines extending beyond Great Britain and to certain activities concerning vessels and construction works in territorial waters).

Regulation 10 Repeals, revocations and modification

Regulation	10

(1) The enactments mentioned in column (1) of Schedule 1 are hereby repealed to the extent specified opposite thereto in column (3) of that Schedule.

(2) The Orders and Regulations mentioned in column 1 of Schedule 2 are hereby revoked to the extent specified opposite thereto in column (3) of that Schedule.

Schedule 1 Repeals

Regulation 10(1)

Schedule 1	(1) Short title	(2) Chapter	(3) Extent of repeal
	The Mines and Quarries Act 1954.	1954 c. 70; relevant amending instrument is SI 1974/2013.	In section 115, the words "section ninety-one (save in so far as it relates to persons employed below ground)" and in paragraph (a) the words "and ninety-one".
	The Agriculture (Safety, Health and Welfare Provisions) Act 1956.	1956 c. 49.	Section 6(1) and (4).
	The Factories Act 1961.	1961 c. 34.	Section 61.
	The Offices, Shops and Railway Premises Act 1963.	1963 c. 41.	Section 24.

Schedule 2 Revocations

Regulation 10(2)

Schedule 2	(1) Regulations or Order	(2) Reference	(3) Extent of revocation
	The Wool, Goat-Hair and Camel-Hair Regulations 1905.	SR & O 1905/1293.	Regulation 15.
	The Horsehair Regulations 1907.	SR & O 1907/984.	Regulation 9(d).
	The Ambulance and First-Aid Arrangements at Blast Furnaces, Copper Mills, Iron Mills, Foundries and Metal Works Order 1917.	SR & O 1917/1067; amended by SR & O 1925/863 and SI 1961/2434.	The whole Order.
	The Saw Mills and Wood-working Factories Welfare (Ambulance and First-aid) Order 1918.	SR & O 1918/1489; amended by SR & O 1925/864 and SI 1961/2434.	The whole Order.
	The Hides and Skins Regulations 1921.	SR & O 1921/2076.	Regulation 1.
	The Chemical Works Regulations 1922.	SR & O 1922/731; relevant amending instruments are SI 1961/2435, 1981/16.	Regulations 10(a), 12, 13, 14 and 17(2)(g).
	Order dated 24th August 1925 revoking provisions in the Ambulance and First-Aid Arrangements at Blast Furnaces, Copper Mills, Iron Mills, Foundries and Metal Works Order 1917.	SR & O 1925/863.	The whole Order.
	Order dated 24th August 1925 revoking provisions in the Saw Mills and Woodworking Factories Welfare (Ambulance and First-aid) Order 1918.	SR & O 1925/864.	The whole Order.

Schedule 2

(1) Regulations or Order	(2) Reference	(3) Extent of revocation
The Herring Curing (Scotland) Welfare Order 1926.	SR & O 1926/535; to which there are amendments not relevant to these Regulations.	Articles 3 and 4.
The Herring Curing Welfare Order 1927.	SR & O 1927/813, amended by SI 1960/1690.	Articles 3 and 4.
The Oil Cake Welfare Order 1929.	SR & O 1929/534.	Article 7.
The Docks Regulations 1934.	SR & O 1934/279, to which there are amendments not relevant to these Regulations.	Regulations 4 to 8.
The Clay Works (Welfare) Special Regulations 1948.	SI 1948/1547.	Regulation 7 and the Schedule.
The Miscellaneous Mines (General) Regulations 1956.	SI 1956/1778.	Regulation 71.
The Quarries (General) Regulations 1956.	SI 1956/1780.	Regulation 38.
The Agriculture (First-aid) Regulations 1957.	SI 1957/940.	The whole Regulations.
The First-aid Boxes in Factories Order 1959.	SI 1959/906; relevant amending instrument is SI 1961/1250.	The whole Order.
The Docks (First-aid Boxes) Order 1959.	SI 1959/2081.	The whole Order.
The First-aid (Standard of Training) Order 1960.	SI 1960/1612; relevant amending instrument is SI 1961/1250.	The whole Order.
The First-aid (Revocation) Regulations 1960.	SI 1960/1690.	The whole Regulations.
The First-aid Boxes (Miscellaneous Industries) Order 1960.	SI 1960/1691.	The whole Order.
The Shipbuilding and Ship-repairing Regulations 1960.	SI 1960/1932, to which there are amendments not relevant to these Regulations.	Regulation 79 and Schedule 3.
The Railway Running Sheds Order 1961.	SI 1961/1250.	Paragraphs 8 and 9 of the Schedule.
The Blast Furnaces and Saw Mills Ambulance (Amendment) Regulations 1961.	SI 1961/2434.	The whole Regulations.

Schedule 2

(1) Regulations or Order	(2) Reference	(3) Extent of revocation
The Chemical Works Ambulance (Amendment) Regulations 1961.	SI 1961/2435.	The whole Regulations.
The Docks (Training in First-aid) Regulations 1962.	SI 1962/241.	The whole Regulations.
The Offices, Shops and Railway Premises First-aid Order 1964.	SI 1964/970; relevant amending instrument is SI 1974/1943.	The whole Order.
The Offices and Shops in Factories (First-aid) Regulations 1964.	SI 1964/1321.	The whole Regulations.
The Offices at Building Operations &c. (First-aid) Regulations 1964.	SI 1964/1322.	The whole Regulations.
The Offices in Electrical Stations (First-aid) Regulations 1964.	SI 1964/1323.	The whole Regulations.
The Information for Employees Regulations 1965.	SI 1965/307.	Paragraph 26 of the Schedule.
The Construction (Health and Welfare) Regulations 1966.	SI 1966/95, amended by SI 1974/209.	In Regulation 3(2), the words from "'certificate in first-aid' does not" to "or over" and from "'training organisation'" to "of these Regulations". In Regulation 4(2), the figures "5, 8, 9". Regulations 5 to 10. The Schedule.
The Ionising Radiations (Unsealed Radioactive Substances) Regulations 1968.	SI 1968/780; to which there are amendments not relevant to these Regulations.	Regulation 44(2).
The Abstract of Factories Act Order 1973.	SI 1973/7.	Paragraph 39 of Schedule 1.
The Factories Act General Register Order 1973.	SI 1973/8.	Part 7 of Schedule 1 and Part 5 of Schedule 2.
The Construction (Health and Welfare) (Amendment) Regulations 1974.	SI 1974/209.	The whole Regulations.

Schedule 2

(1) Regulations or Order	(2) Reference	(3) Extent of revocation
The Offices, Shops and Railway Premises Act 1963 (Repeals and Modifications) Regulations 1974.	SI 1974/1943.	Regulation 3(2).
The Chemical Works (Metrication) Regulations 1981.	SI 1981/16.	All entries in the Schedule relating to regulation 12 of the Chemical Works Regulations 1922.

Appendix 1 Record of first-aid provision

First-aid personnel	Required Yes/no	Number needed
Appointed person		
First-aider with an emergency first aid at work certificate		
First-aider with a first aid at work certificate		
First-aider with additional training (specify)		
First-aid equipment and facilities	**Required Yes/no**	**Number needed**
Dust- and damp-proof first-aid container		
Kit contents		
Additional equipment (specify), eg foil blankets, eye wash bottles, shears, microporous tape, tourniquets, haemostatic dressings		
Defibrillator		
Travelling first-aid kit		
First-aid room		

Note: The minimum first-aid provision for each worksite is:

- a person appointed to take charge of first-aid arrangements;
- a suitably stocked first-aid kit;
- information for all employees about what they need to do in case of an emergency.

Appendix 2 First-aid kits

1   **There is no mandatory list of items to be included in a first-aid container**. The decision on what to provide will be influenced by the findings of the first-aid needs assessment. As a guide, where work activities involve low hazards, a

minimum stock of first-aid items might be:

■   a leaflet giving general guidance on first aid (for example, HSE's leaflet *Basic advice on first aid at work*);[6]
■   20 individually wrapped sterile plasters (assorted sizes), appropriate to the type of work (hypoallergenic plasters can be provided if necessary);
■   two sterile eye pads;
■   two individually wrapped triangular bandages, preferably sterile;
■   six safety pins;
■   two large, sterile, individually wrapped unmedicated wound dressings;
■   six medium-sized sterile individually wrapped unmedicated wound dressings;
■   at least three pairs of disposable gloves (see HSE's leaflet *Latex and you*).[7]

2   Employers may wish to refer to British Standard BS 8599 which provides further information on the contents of workplace first-aid kits. Whether using a first-aid kit complying with BS 8599 or an alternative kit, the contents should reflect the outcome of the first-aid needs assessment.

Travelling first-aid kit contents

3   There is no mandatory list of items to be included in first-aid kits for travelling workers. They might typically contain:

■   a leaflet giving general guidance on first aid (for example HSE's leaflet *Basic advice on first aid at work*);[6]
■   six individually wrapped sterile plasters (hypoallergenic plasters can be provided, if necessary);
■   two individually wrapped triangular bandages, preferably sterile;
■   two safety pins;
■   one large, sterile, unmedicated dressing;
■   individually wrapped moist cleansing wipes;
■   two pairs of disposable gloves (see HSE's leaflet *Latex and you*).[7]

4   Either of the above should be considered as suggested contents lists only.

Appendix 3 Suggested numbers of first-aid personnel to be available at all times people are at work

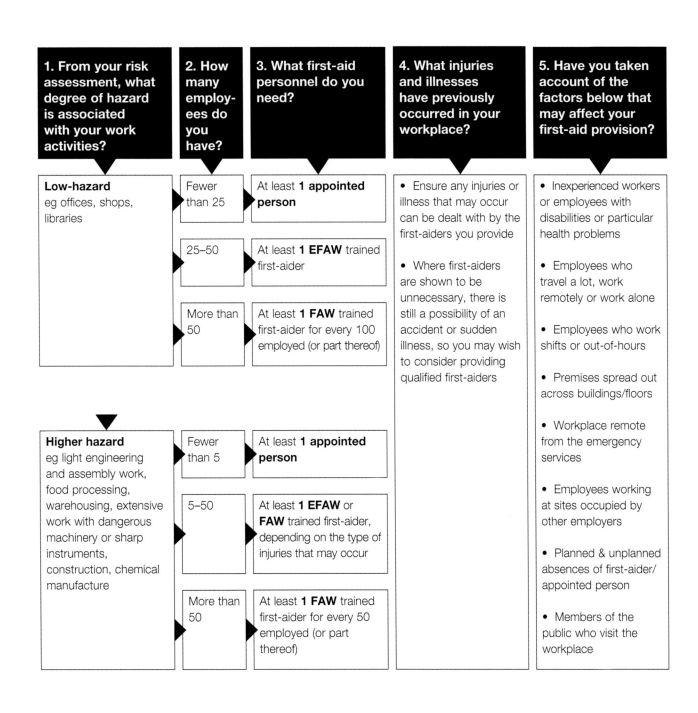

1. From your risk assessment, what degree of hazard is associated with your work activities?	2. How many employ-ees do you have?	3. What first-aid personnel do you need?	4. What injuries and illnesses have previously occurred in your workplace?	5. Have you taken account of the factors below that may affect your first-aid provision?
Low-hazard eg offices, shops, libraries	Fewer than 25	At least **1 appointed person**	• Ensure any injuries or illness that may occur can be dealt with by the first-aiders you provide • Where first-aiders are shown to be unnecessary, there is still a possibility of an accident or sudden illness, so you may wish to consider providing qualified first-aiders	• Inexperienced workers or employees with disabilities or particular health problems • Employees who travel a lot, work remotely or work alone • Employees who work shifts or out-of-hours • Premises spread out across buildings/floors • Workplace remote from the emergency services • Employees working at sites occupied by other employers • Planned & unplanned absences of first-aider/ appointed person • Members of the public who visit the workplace
	25–50	At least **1 EFAW** trained first-aider		
	More than 50	At least **1 FAW** trained first-aider for every 100 employed (or part thereof)		
Higher hazard eg light engineering and assembly work, food processing, warehousing, extensive work with dangerous machinery or sharp instruments, construction, chemical manufacture	Fewer than 5	At least **1 appointed person**		
	5–50	At least **1 EFAW** or **FAW** trained first-aider, depending on the type of injuries that may occur		
	More than 50	At least **1 FAW** trained first-aider for every 50 employed (or part thereof)		

Appendix 4 Additional training that may be required after a first-aid needs assessment

Table 3 Table of examples of additional training needs

Additional training	When additional training may be relevant
Management of a casualty suffering from hypothermia or hyperthermia	Extensive exposure to the outdoor environment due to, for example, regular maintenance activity, eg trackside rail work, forestry
Management of a casualty suffering from hydrofluoric acid burns	Glass industry, chemical manufacture, or other industries using pickling pastes containing hydrofluoric acid
Management of a casualty suffering from cyanide poisoning	Chemical manufacture
Oxygen administration	Confined space work, for example tank cleaning operations and working in sewers. Also, where there is a risk of exposure to hydrogen cyanide
Management of a drowning casualty	Swimming pools, fish farms
Application of haemostatic dressings and/or tourniquets	Sectors such as agriculture, forestry and construction Employers of people working in hospitality, events or other relevant sectors might wish to consider additional training to prepare for injuries to colleagues or the public, resulting from terrorist acts or other violent incidents
Recognise the presence of major illness and provide appropriate first aid (including heart attack, stroke, epilepsy, asthma, diabetes)	Wherever the environment is low hazard but you have identified a risk, either based on the known health profile, age and number of employees or a need to consider members of the public
Paediatric first aid, as required by the Department for Education or local authorities, which complies with the syllabus produced by OFSTED for first-aid provision for children in a school or other childcare setting	Schools and nurseries

In addition to the above, when working in areas where you have significant exposure to members of the public but are classified as low hazard you may wish to consider EFAW training, as listed in Appendix 6, and the management of major illness.

Appendix 5 Content of a first aid at work (FAW) course

On completion of training, whether a full FAW course or a FAW requalification course, successful candidates should have satisfactorily demonstrated competence in all of the subject areas listed in Appendix 6 and also to be able to:

■ administer first aid to a casualty with:
  – injuries to bones, muscles and joints, including suspected spinal injuries;
  – chest injuries;
  – burns and scalds;
  – eye injuries;
  – sudden poisoning;
  – anaphylactic shock;
■ recognise the presence of major illness (including heart attack, stroke, epilepsy, asthma, diabetes) and provide appropriate first aid.

Appendix 6 Content of an emergency first aid at work (EFAW) course

On completion of training, successful candidates should be able to:

■ understand the role of the first-aider, including reference to:
   – the importance of preventing cross infection;
   – the need for recording incidents and actions;
   – use of available equipment;
■ assess the situation and circumstances in order to act safely, promptly and effectively in an emergency;
■ administer first aid to a casualty who is unconscious (including seizure);
■ administer cardiopulmonary resuscitation and use an automated external defibrillator;
■ administer first aid to a casualty who is choking;
■ administer first aid to a casualty who is wounded and bleeding;
■ administer first aid to a casualty who is suffering from shock;
■ provide appropriate first aid for minor injuries (including small cuts, grazes and bruises, minor burns and scalds, small splinters).

Appendix 7 Suggested content of annual refresher course

Suggested course content for annual refresher training:

- Assess the situation and circumstances in order to act safely, promptly and effectively in an emergency.
- Administer first aid to a casualty who is unconscious (including seizure).
- Administer cardiopulmonary resuscitation.
- Administer first aid to a casualty who is wounded and bleeding.
- Administer first aid to a casualty who is suffering from shock.

References

1   Risk assessment: www.hse.gov.uk/risk

2   *Reporting accidents and incidents at work: A brief guide to the Reporting of Injuries, Diseases and Dangerous Occurrences Regulations 2013 (RIDDOR)* Leaflet INDG453(rev1) HSE Books 2013 www.hse.gov.uk/pubns/indg453.htm (see also www.hse.gov.uk/riddor)

3   *Safety signs and signals. The Health and Safety (Safety Signs and Signals) Regulations 1996. Guidance on Regulations* L64 (Second edition) HSE Books 2009 ISBN 978 0 7176 6359 0 www.hse.gov.uk/pubns/books/l64.htm

4   *Provision and Use of Work Equipment Regulations 1998 (PUWER). Approved Code of Practice and guidance* L22 (Fourth edition) HSE Books 2014 ISBN 978 0 7176 6619 5 www.hse.gov.uk/pubns/priced/l22

5   *Selecting a first-aid training provider: A guide for employers* Information Sheet GEIS3 HSE 2018 www.hse.gov.uk/pubns/geis3.htm

6   *Basic advice on first aid at work* Leaflet INDG347 HSE Books 2017 www.hse.gov.uk/pubns/indg347.htm

7   *Latex and you* Leaflet INDG320 HSE 2000 www.hse.gov.uk/pubns/indg320.htm

Further reading

First aid at mines. Health and Safety (First-Aid) Regulations 1981. Approved Code of Practice L43 HSE Books 1993 ISBN 978 0 7176 0617 7 www.hse.gov.uk/pubns/books/l43.htm

Data Protection Act 1998 The Stationery Office 1998 ISBN 978 0 10 542998 2 www.legislation.gov.uk

Accident book BL510 HSE Books 2012 ISBN 978 0 7176 6458 0 www.hse.gov.uk/pubns/books/accident-book.htm

First aid at work: Your questions answered Leaflet INDG214 HSE Books 2014 www.hse.gov.uk/pubns/indg214.htm

Basic advice on first aid at work Poster HSE Books 2017 www.hse.gov.uk/pubns/books/first-aid-poster.htm

Electric shock: First aid procedures Poster HSE Books 2017 www.hse.gov.uk/pubns/books/electric-shock-poster.htm

Further information

For information about health and safety visit https://books.hse.gov.uk or http://www.hse.gov.uk. You can view HSE guidance online and order priced publications from the website. HSE priced publications are also available from bookshops.

To report inconsistencies or inaccuracies in this guidance email: commissioning@wlt.com.

British Standards can be obtained in PDF or hard copy formats from BSI: http://shop.bsigroup.com or by contacting BSI Customer Services for hard copies only Tel: 0846 086 9001 email: cservices@bsigroup.com.

The Stationery Office publications are available from The Stationery Office, PO Box 29, Norwich NR3 1GN Tel: 0333 202 5070 Fax: 0333 202 5080. E-mail:customer.services@tso.co.uk Website: www.tso.co.uk. They are also available from bookshops.

Statutory Instruments can be viewed free of charge at www.legislation.gov.uk where you can also search for changes to legislation.

Information on first aid at work is available on HSE's website at: www.hse.gov.uk/firstaid

This guidance is available online at www.hse.gov.uk/pubns/books/l74.htm

To report an accident or an incident go to www.hse.gov.uk/riddor/report.htm and complete the appropriate online report form. The form will then be submitted directly to the RIDDOR database. You will receive a copy for your records. For fatalities and major injuries only call the Incident Contact Centre on

03845 300 9923 (opening hours Monday to Friday 8.30 am to 5 pm).

Information on the training in the use of automated external defibrillators is available from the Resuscitation Council (UK) at www.resus.org.uk